# FIGHT
## FOR LOVE

SMALL GROUP ST

# FIGHT

## FOR LOVE

Vanessa Russell

COPYRIGHT

# *FORWARD*

I THANK MY LORD AND SAVIOR JESUS

FOR CONTINUED REVELATION, HEALING AND RESTORATION.  I ALSO THANK . . .

MY HUSBAND, PASTOR TIMOTHY RUSSELL, AND MY CHILDREN FOR THE DAILY SUPPORT AND PERSONAL SACRIFICES THEY HAVE MADE AS I PURSUE MY PURPOSE AND USE

MY TESTIMONY TO SET OTHERS LIKE ME FREE.

MY FAMILY, FRIENDS AND CHURCH FAMILY (#HOPE4HAYWARD) WHO CONTINUE TO ENCOURAGE ME TO WALK IN THE FULLNESS OF GOD'S PURPOSE.

LOVE NEVER FAILS LOVENEVERFAILSUS.COM

STAFF, VOLUNTEERS, AND PARTNERS, WHO ACTIVELY WALK IN LOVE FOR THOSE WHO ARE HURTING IN OUR WORLD.

THE SURVIVOR LEADERS WHO COURAGEOUSLY FACE THE WORLD EVERY DAY DESPITE THEIR DIFFICULT EXPERIENCES AND WHO CONTINUE TO LEND THEIR VOICE TO

THIS FIGHT FOR LOVE.

FEET FIRST FOUNDATION OF MARTINEZ, CALIFORNIA FOR BELIEVING IN THE CALLING ON MY LIFE AND INTRODUCING ME TO NEW LIFE CHURCH OF ALAMO, CA,

CREATING AN OPEN DOOR FOR THIS WORK TO GO FORTH.

MY CELEBRATE RECOVERY SPONSORS DEBORAH RICO AND KATHY WAECHTLER.

BOTH SUPPORTED ME WHE I WORKED MY STEPS IN 2009.

SABLE HORTON AND BELOVED ALVAREZ FOR CONTRIBUTING THEIR POWERFUL POETRY INCLUDED IN THE APPENDIX.

*"THERE IS ONE PERSON WORTH FIGHTING FOR, AND JESUS SAID IT'S YOU!"*

# *INTRODUCTION*

As a survivor of sexual, physical, and emotional abuse, childhood neglect, foster care, and domestic violence, I know first hand what it's like to feel unworthy of love. For many years I lived a life that reflected what I experienced rather than who I really was. I am elated to share Celebrate Recovery's twelve steps with you with specific insight

into how the steps apply to healing from abuse, domestic violence and human trafficking. I believe the time you spend with God reflecting on these stories and biblical truths will lead to a miraculous healing and your complete restoration.

I want to reassure you that though this pursuit of love promises to be difficult, there is one person who is worth fighting and Jesus said it's YOU!

# TABLE OF CONTENTS

# SMALL GROUP PURPOSE STATEMENT

Fight for Love Small Group Study is a twelve-week study that is designed to help you heal from abuse, domestic violence and/or human trafficking.

It is my prayer that you will receive the healing and restoration that God designed for you as you come to understand who you really are.

I believe that you will experience miraculous healing even now as you come to understand how deeply you are loved and that past hurts, habits, and hang-ups will be used to set others like you free.

> *What the enemy meant for bad God uses for good.*
>
> — *Genesis 50:20*

**Fight for Love Small Group Facilitators:**

You can access the free Fight For Love Facilitator Guide, Author Facilitated Guide, Fight For Love marketplace and other online resources at:

*loveneverfailsus.com/FightForLove.*

Also please read the "Facilitator Best Practices" in the Appendix for tips on how to support participants through this journey.

# FIGHT FOR LOVE

# SMALL GROUP GUIDELINES AND THE SMALL GROUP COVENANT

Fight for Love small groups need to be safe places in order to achieve their purpose.

As such, we will embrace Celebrate Recovery's Small Group Guidelines (Baker 2007) which are as follows:

1. Keep your sharing focused on your own thoughts and feelings.

2. Each person is free to express feelings without interruption.

3. We are here to support one another. We will not attempt to fix one another.

4. Anonymity and confidentiality are basic requirements. What is shared in the group stays in the group! The only exception is when someone threatens to harm themselves or others.

5. All Fight-for-Love Small Groups are same sex groups.


The Fight for Love Small Group Study Covenant does the following:

1. Ensures that your group is safe for participants to share their hurts, habits and hang-ups.

2. Unifies attendees with the Lord and each other, giving them the strength to allow the Lord to complete the healing process.

# SMALL GROUP COVENANT

I will attend all twelve weeks and come to the meeting prepared, ensuring that my lesson for the week is filled out and I have completed at least one self-care activity.

*All you need to say is simply 'Yes' or 'No.'*

*— Matthew 5:37*

I will pray daily for each of the individuals in my group. (Baker 2007) 2 Chronicles 7:14 –If my people, who are called by my name, will humble themselves and pray and seek my face and turn from their wicked ways, then I will hear from heaven, and I will forgive their sin and will heal their land.

I will honor the individuals in my group by adhering to the small group guidelines.

*Love your neighbor as yourself.*

*— Matthew 22:39*

I will seek out additional help with my hurts, habits  and hang-ups as I await complete healing. A dear friend, Pastor Richard Guest, shared a powerful sermon based on John 5. He encouraged us to believe that God can miraculously heal us in certain seasons and yet while we are waiting, we are released and encouraged to seek wisdom and care from medical and clinical professionals.

*After these things there was a feast of the Jews, and Jesus went up to Jerusalem. 2 Now there is in Jerusalem by the sheep gate a pool, which is called in Hebrew Bethesda, having five porticoes. 3 In these lay a multitude of those who were sick, blind, lame, and withered, waiting for the moving of the waters; 4 for an angel of the Lord went down at certain seasons into the pool and stirred up the water; whoever then first, after the stirring up of the water, stepped in was made well from whatever disease with which he was afflicted. 5 A man was there who had been ill for thirty-eight years. 6 When Jesus saw him lying there, and knew that he had already been a long time in that condition, He said to him, "Do you wish to get well?" 7 The sick man answered Him, "Sir, I have no man to put me into the pool when the water is stirred up, but while I am coming, another steps down before me." 8 Jesus said to him, "Get up, pick up your pallet and walk." 9 Immediately the man became well, and picked up his pallet and began to walk.*

*— John 5:1*

I will ask a member of the same sex in my group to be my accountability partner.

*Therefore confess your sins to each other and pray for each other so that you may be healed. The prayer of a righteous person is powerful and effective.*

*— James 5:16*

# FIGHT FOR LOVE SMALL GROUP COVENANT

Please initial each covenant below and sign at the bottom:

_____ I will attend all twelve weeks and come to the meeting prepared, ensuring that my lesson for the week is complete. *All you need to say is simply 'Yes' or 'No.' — Matthew 5:37*

_____ I will pray daily for each of the individuals in my group. (Baker 2007) *If my people, who are called by my name, will humble themselves and pray and seek my face and turn from their wicked ways, then I will hear from heaven, and I will forgive their sin and will heal their land. — 2 Chronicles 7:14*

_____ I will honor the individuals in my group by adhering to the small group guidelines. *Love your neighbor as yourself. — Matthew 22:39*

_____ I will seek out additional help with my hurts, habits and hang ups as I await complete healing.

*After these things there was a feast of the Jews, and Jesus went up to Jerusalem. 2 Now there is in Jerusalem by the sheep gate a pool, which is called in Hebrew Bethesda, having five porticoes. 3 In these lay a multitude of those who were sick, blind, lame, and withered, waiting for the moving of the waters; 4 for an angel of the Lord went down at certain seasons into the pool and stirred up the water; whoever then first, after the stirring up of the water, stepped in was made well from whatever disease with which he was afflicted. 5 A man was there who had been ill for thirty-eight years. 6 When Jesus saw him lying there, and knew that he had already been a long time in that condition, He said to him, "Do you wish to get well?" 7 The sick man answered Him, "Sir, I have no man to put me into the pool when the water is stirred up, but while I am coming, another steps down before me." 8 Jesus said to him, "Get up, pick up your pallet and walk." 9 Immediately the man became well, and picked up his pallet and began to walk.*

*— John 5: 1*

_____ I will ask a member of the same sex in my group to be my accountability partner.

*Therefore confess your sins to each other and pray for each other so that you may be healed. The prayer of a righteous person is powerful and effective.*

*— James 5:16*

## FIGHT FOR LOVE SMALL GROUP PARTICIPANT

Name _____

Signed _____

Date _____

## FIGHT FOR LOVE SMALL GROUP FACILITATOR

Name _____

Signed _____

Date _____

*You are now ready to start the Fight for Love!*

# FUNDAMENTALS OF SEXUAL ABUSE, DOMESTIC VIOLENCE AND HUMAN TRAFFICKING

Before we begin, it is important that we define each of the areas of abuse that this program was specifically designed to address.

In general, sexual, physical, and emotional abuse, domestic violence and human trafficking often involve a misuse of power and control. This chart describes the kind of behaviors that are experienced and demonstrated in this cycle.

**POWER AND CONTROL**

### Coercion, Threats & Purposeful Manipulation

- Threatening friends and family
- Harming another person for victim's disobedience
- Learning & exploiting victim's insecurities

### Isolation and Emotional Violence

- Isolating victim from support system
- Shaming and humiliating
- Unfamiliar with/unaware of geographic location

### Sexual and Physical Violence

- Torturing, threatening, branding, tattooing victim

- Forcing drug use, denying food or bathroom
- Raping and/or forcing into human trafficking

**Economic Dependence**

- Refusing to allow victim to go to school or work
- Taking money & belongings from victim
- Giving money to family for "right to abuse" victim

The definition of each type of abuse we will discuss is as follows:

## SEXUAL ABUSE

Sexual abuse is any sort of non-consensual sexual contact. Sexual abuse can happen to men or women of any age. Sex with a child is ALWAYS non-consensual and abusive. Sexual abuse can include derogatory name calling, forcing someone to have sex when they do not want to— even when it's their wife or husband— deliberately causing unwanted physical pain during sex, deliberately passing on sexual diseases or infections, and using objects without consent and to cause pain or humiliation.

Child Sexual Abuse is any sexual act with a child performed by an adult or an older child. Child sexual abuse could be but is not limited to the following:

- Sexual touching of any part of the body, clothed or unclothed;
- Encouraging a child to engage in any sexual activity, including masturbation;
- Intentionally engaging in sexual activity in front of a child even if it

can only be heard;

- Showing children pornography, or using children to create pornography;

- Encouraging a child to engage in sex in exchange for money or goods. This is called Commercial Sexual Exploitation of a Child (CSEC).

Here are some statistics that help us to understand the prevalence of sexual abuse in our world. (Leshner 1998) (USDHHS 2006) (DOJ 1999)

**BEFORE THEY TURN 18 . . .**

**1 IN 6 BOYS** experience
some form of sexual abuse

**1 IN 4 GIRLS** experience
some form of sexual abuse

- A child abuse report is made every ten seconds.

- Child abuse occurs at every socioeconomic level, across ethnic and cultural lines, within all religions and at all levels of education.

- More than 90% of juvenile sexual abuse victims know their perpetrator in some way.

- About 80% of 21-year-olds who were abused as children meet criteria for at least one psychological disorder like depression or anxiety.

- Children whose parent's abuse alcohol and other drugs are three times more likely to be abused.

- Abused children are 25% more likely to experience teen pregnancy.

- Abused teens are less likely to practice safe sex, putting them at greater risk for STDs.

Knowing these statistics helped me to realize that I was not alone in my experience and in the destructive behaviors that I allowed in my life as a result of the abuse. The good news is we no longer have to suffer in silence or carry shame and unwanted behaviors that are not ours to own.

Together we can declare that this is an epidemic that impacts 1/4 of our world and we are able to conquer it with the love of Christ.

*I can do all things through Christ who strengthens me*

*— Philippians 4:13.*

## PHYSICAL ABUSE

Physical abuse is any intentional act causing physical injury to another person. Physical abuse can range from spitting on a person or pushing them to homicide. Legally physical abuse can be considered assault and lead to homicide.

## EMOTIONAL ABUSE

Emotional abuse is forced isolation, verbal put downs, humiliation or intimidation. This behavior often results is the abused feeling worthless and sometimes suicidal. This abuse can exist separate from physical and sexual abuse and human trafficking but is often part of the situation where those types of abuses exist.


## DOMESTIC VIOLENCE

According to the National Coalition against Domestic Violence, 1 in 4 women will be victims of domestic violence at some point in their lives, and 1.3 million women are assaulted by their partner every year.

Domestic violence and emotional abuse are used to control a partner. Partners may be married or not married; heterosexual, gay, or lesbian; living together, separated or dating and the perpetrator of the violence can be any gender. There is sometimes a cross section between domestic violence and human trafficking where the relationship starts off as abusive and accelerates into selling the abused person for personal gain.

**Domestic violence and abuse can include the following behaviors:**

- Name-calling or putdowns

- Isolating partner from family or friends

- Withholding or taking money

- Keeping a partner from getting or keeping a job

- Physical harm or threats to do so

- Sexual assault or threats to do so

- Stalking

- Intimidation

Domestic violence can be criminal, including physical assault, sexual abuse (unwanted or forced sexual activity), and stalking. Although emotional, psychological and financial abuse are not criminal behaviors, they are forms of abuse and can lead to criminal violence and, if they persist, can become criminal.

Domestic violence can happen one time a month or many times a day and it can happen to anyone regardless of age, gender, race, culture, religion, education, socioeconomic status, etc.

In addition, domestic violence can be perpetrated by a man or woman.


## HUMAN TRAFFICKING

Human Trafficking, also known as modern day slavery, is the act of treating someone unfairly and abusively in order to benefit from their work. This unfair treatment can include selling them for sex and/or forcing them to work for little or no pay in inhumane working conditions.

The United Nations defines human trafficking using three criteria (Nations 2018):

It involves an **ACT**: A transaction occurs involving the recruiting, transporting and/or holding of a victim.

It is executed by any **MEANS** necessary: A method is used to obtain and retain the victim including tricking them, forcing them or threatening them.

It has a destructive **PURPOSE**: The goal of human trafficking is to execute personal gain for one at the expense of another.

Statistically speaking, human trafficking has become more and more common. According to the United Nations, there are between 27 and 30 million modern-day slaves in the world, making it the fastest growing enterprise in the world, generating $150B a year.

Many people think that human trafficking is something that only happens overseas, but that is a myth. According to the National Human Trafficking Hotline, the majority of human trafficking victims in the United States are U.S. citizens. (Polaris 2017)

Many victims do not initially identify as human trafficking survivors and do not fully understand the way in which they were tricked, forced, or threatened.

These steps will help each survivor to process what they have experienced and give it a name so they can be healed and used to heal others.

**If you would like to exit the life or know someone who does,**

**you can contact the**

National Human Trafficking Hotline 888-3737-888 or text BE-FREE.

You can also contact

**Love Never Fails @ 844-249-2698**

www.loveneverfailsus.com

facebook.com/loveneverfailsfanpage

twitter.com/LoveNeverFails5

instagram.com/loveneverfailsus

You can also listen to our weekly radio broadcast.

To find out when we are on air, go to facebook.com/loveneverfailsradio

# GROUND ZERO

Are you a survivor of abuse, domestic violence and/or human trafficking?

Before we can get started on the steps it's important that we address a lie that you've been carrying around your entire life.

That lie is that you are responsible for your abuse.

If as a child you were sexually, physically, or emotionally abused, you are not responsible for that abuse.

If you were trafficked as a child you are not responsible for that abuse.

I want to you speak it out loud. Repeat after me:

**I am not responsible for my abuse.**
**I deserve to live a life free**
**from shame and blame.**
**I claim my healing today.**

If you are a victim of adult rape, domestic violence or human trafficking, during this process you may find that you may self-blame and experience shame about these incidents because of who you were associating with, the behaviors and addictions you were engaged in, and/or the dangers that you did not see.

You might think, "was so stupid." Thoughts of, "I woulda, shoulda, coulda prevented this" will inevitably pop up.

When this happens, I urge you to consider whether the child abuse you experienced is the root cause of the destructive behaviors you are acting out as an adult.

If you were abused as a child and you believe it is causing you to act out in dangerous ways, remember you are not responsible for any abuse committed against you as a child.

That said, now that we are adults we are empowered to take ownership of our lives.

A powerful way to do that is to make amends with ourselves and with those who we have harmed in any way. The steps will guide you through this process. As you are walking through this book, don't allow that internal critical voice to drown out love.

I urge you to fight to love yourself more than you blame yourself and to move to a place of forgiveness.

*Above all, love each other deeply, because*
*love covers over a multitude of sins.*

*— 1 Peter 4:8*

# STEP 1

## WEEK 1 ASSIGNMENTS

☐ Sign Covenant if you haven't done so already. Read Fight for Love Introduction.

☐ Read Fight for Love Principle, Scripture, Prayer, Small Group Study Overview, Week 1 Questions and Personal Testimonial.

☐ As you've committed, please be sure to complete Week 1 Small Group Study Questions in detail prior to next week's meeting.

☐ Write down personal reflections and prayer requests that come up during the week.

☐ Complete at least one activity.

☐ Sign Covenant if you haven't done so already. Read Fight for Love Introduction.

## PRINCIPLE

We admitted we were powerless over our addictions and compulsive behaviors, that our lives had become unmanageable. (Baker 2007)

## SCRIPTURE

*I know that nothing good lives in me, that is, in my sinful nature. For I have the desire to do what is good, but I cannot carry it out.*

**PRAYER**

Father in heaven, I pray that you assist me in acknowledging that I do not have the power that I wish I had and that I need you to help me conquer the addictions and compulsive behaviors that have made my life unmanageable. In Jesus' name, amen.

**WEEK 1 — SMALL GROUP STUDY OVERVIEW**

Congratulations! You've taken the first step by admitting you need help. Romans 7:18 is so real. It says, "I desire to do what is good but I can't carry it out." Many times we convince ourselves that we can control our negative behaviors, but what ends up happening is we become addicted to unmanageable, controlling behaviors that are difficult for others to tolerate. If we would only let Jesus do it . . . if we would only let him deliver us from the behavior . . . show us the root cause and how to pray, then we would know true healing and freedom.

**WEEK 1 — SMALL GROUP STUDY QUESTIONS**

**What do you have power over?**

**Name three goals that you have struggled to achieve over the last 12 months.**

**Goal 1:**

Goal 2:



Goal 3:



What is your motivation for each goal?

*Motivation 1:*


*Motivation 2:*



*Motivation 3:*



Why do you think you've struggled to accomplish these goals?



What addictions or compulsive behaviors do you struggle with?

**What would your most trusted friend say is your greatest struggle?**



**Is your life unmanageable? In what way?**



## PERSONAL TESTIMONY

Years ago I was involved in an abusive relationship with a drug addicted man. I went back to him at least 20 times over an eight-year period. I was stuck, and I remember my family and friends questioning me and wondering if I had some mental illness that kept me in a vicious cycle of extreme happiness, followed by abuse and extreme depression. Every time I went back I returned for the same reasons. I was emotionally starved and wanted to be loved so badly that I blocked out of my mind the abuse that would begin almost instantly after the honeymoon stage was over. I remember an incident that helped me find deliverance from the relationship. I let him move back in with me after he lost another job. He was sleeping and said he had a cold but I remember thinking he was high. One of the terms of him moving back in was that he would stop using and get a job and keep it. Despite this, there he was, sleeping in a robe all day long as I worked and provided for the family. I was irritated but tried to be sympathetic. He was sick, right? I had recently given my life to the Lord and I heard a new voice who I now know was God. He told me to go outside. I began walking toward the door. It was dark outside. He told me to get in my boyfriend's car. I opened the door and got in the driver seat. It was very dark and I couldn't see anything. He told me to reach out my hand and there I encountered a huge bag of drugs. It was the final push I needed.

There was no big blow up. Just a loving God who shared with me that I was powerless to see the destruction that was ahead, and powerless to deliver myself from the love addiction I was experiencing. It took our great God to get my attention and set me free.

## WEEK 1 — TAKE ACTION

This week take some time to engage in one of the activities below and journal the process you used to get it done and whether it was difficult or easy.

- Pray

- Boxing

- Art

- Do something new

- Serve/give back

- Poetry – See Appendix for two beautiful poems.

- Dance

- Affirmation

- Cook

- Advocate

- Write your testimony

- Make a video

## WEEK 1 — REFLECTION

**Participant Prayer Requests**

# *STEP 2*

## WEEK 2 ASSIGNMENTS

☐ Read answers to questions from Week 1.

☐ Read Fight for Love Principle, Scripture, Prayer, Small Group Study Overview, Week 2 Questions and Personal Testimonial.

☐ As you've committed, please be sure to complete Week 2 Small Group Study Questions in detail prior to next week's meeting.

☐ Write down personal reflections and prayer requests that come up during the week.

☐ Complete at least one activity.

## PRINCIPLE

We came to believe that a power greater than ourselves could restore us to sanity. (Baker 2007)

## SCRIPTURE

*For it is God who works in you to will and to act according to his good purpose.*

*— Philippians 2:13*

## PRAYER

Father in heaven, you have created us in your image and designed us with purpose. I pray your word over myself and declare that no weapon formed against me shall prosper. I declare that those things that have removed my sanity do not have the final say and that you who are the author and finisher of my faith have power over everything that has kept me bound, and that you will restore me in your perfect timing and with your perfect hand of love and grace. In Jesus' name, amen.

## WEEK 2 — SMALL GROUP STUDY OVERVIEW

Did you know that your purpose is greater than your pain; that every tear that you have shed that has stolen your peace and sanity will be used for the glory of God?

I used to wonder, "Why Me?" and feel sorry for myself. I would think about being raped at the age of 12 and the aftermath. I was so full of shame and anxiety I could barely sleep. I filled my days with "aholic" behavior, throwing myself into a plate a food, a toxic relationship, or an abusive and thankless job, to feel worthy and alive. Every now and then I would watch a feel-good movie or read a self-help article and think it was just the inspiration I needed to change, but after a few moments I would be right back at the same depressing place of defeat, overwhelmed with even more shame because now I had failed at failing.

It wasn't until I stopped leaning on my own understanding and power that I began to see that I could not reason myself out of pain. Instead, I had to let God heal me.

# WEEK 2 — SMALL GROUP STUDY QUESTIONS

Have you ever tried to change an unwanted behavior or addiction?

How long were you able to maintain that change on your own power?

Have you ever tried to start a new positive behavior? How long were you able to maintain that change on your own power?

Has God delivered you from behaviors that you could not change on your own?

What does the principle mean when it says, "a power higher than yourself can restore you to sanity?"

What is the purpose that God has assigned to your life?

**How has God changed your desires and behaviors to line up with your purpose?**

## PERSONAL TESTIMONY

When I was 14, my boyfriend introduced me to crack cocaine. In a matter of weeks I cleared out the savings account I had been building up for almost a year. I rapidly sank into a dark hole and began compromising things and relationships that I valued to get high. I was spending time in crack houses and hanging out with drug dealers, exploiters and victims of human trafficking. I had not yet been sold but was being propositioned and considering ways to support my addiction. I was losing touch with reality and very close to falling away. One day my mom and I got into a fight. I refused to go to school and she kept yelling at me to get out of bed and started calling me names. I became enraged and hit her. She called the police and they placed me in a mental hospital for two weeks where I detoxed. There I decided I would stop smoking crack and stop seeing that boyfriend. I believe God gave me the fortitude to stop when he revealed to me that I was going to "fiend now or fiend later . . . no matter what, I was going to fiend." Knowing that the pain was unavoidable and that it would only get worse helped me to fiend right then and I never went back.

I didn't know the Lord then so I suppose I thought I quit on my own, but when I look back I realize the life or death choice I was given was a revelation from the Lord and it has sustained me even until now.

# WEEK 2 — TAKE ACTION

This week ask God to help you engage in one of the activities below, or in something else that he puts on your heart. Share with the group how it felt to surrender this to the Lord.

- Pray

- Boxing

- Art

- Do something new

- Serve/give back

- Poetry – See Appendix for two beautiful poems.

- Dance

- Affirmation

- Cook

- Journal

- Advocate

- Write your testimony

- Make a video

- Week 2 Reflection

# WEEK 2 — REFLECTION

## Participant Prayer Requests

# STEP 3

## WEEK 3 ASSIGNMENTS

☐ Read answers to questions from Week 2.

☐ Read Fight for Love Principle, Scripture, Prayer, Small Group Study Overview, Week 3 Questions and Personal Testimonial.

☐ As you've committed, please be sure to complete Week 3 Small Group Study Questions in detail prior to next week's meeting.

☐ Write down personal reflections and prayer requests that come up during the week.

☐ Complete at least one activity.

## PRINCIPLE

We made a decision to turn our lives and our wills over to the care of God. (Baker 2007)

## SCRIPTURE

*Therefore, I urge you, brothers, in view of God's mercy, to offer your bodies as living sacrifices, holy and pleasing to God — this is your spiritual act of worship.*

*—Romans 12:1*

**PRAYER**

Father in heaven, I give up. I can no longer pretend that I know how to live this life without you. I need your guidance and wisdom. I need your love and acceptance. I need your strength and endurance. Everything that I am that is good comes from you and I wait for your direction over every step that I take.

Take me, dear Lord, into your loving hands and show me how to live. In Jesus' name, amen.

## WEEK 3 — SMALL GROUP STUDY OVERVIEW

Jesus is gentle. He doesn't force us to live according to his plan, but when we decide to turn our lives over to him, we open ourselves to receive a gift so much greater than the thing we were afraid to lose. Mark 8:35 says those who try to gain their own life will *lose it*; but those who lose their life for Jesus' sake will *gain it*. Sounds crazy right? But it's true. If we surrender the things that we think we need and the things that we think we know in exchange for the plan of God, we will not only understand his purpose but receive the power we need to fulfill it.

# WEEK 3 — SMALL GROUP STUDY QUESTIONS

Describe how you make decisions. What is your process? Do you think about it, research it, or just do it?

Do you pray before making decisions? If so, do you find that it improves the outcome?

How much does God care for you? Can you trust him with your life?

Have you ever been mad at God and blamed him for something that happened only to realize that your horrible experience was used to bring you closer to your purpose?

Do you have a general idea of your purpose? How was this revealed to you?

## PERSONAL TESTIMONY

My son's best friend passed away at the age of 17. Ironically, I had planned out both of their lives for years. I planned that they would be best man for each other and godfather to each other's children. I imagined them supporting one another, hanging out on the weekends, going away on family vacations, etc. And then one afternoon I got the news. Our precious beautiful one had gone to be with the Lord.

I realized then that my ways are not God's ways and my thoughts are not God's thoughts. I had planned out my entire life and the life of everyone I knew and actually thought I could control our future. After this young man passed, I went through months (or years) of grief. I still battle these feelings from time to time, but more than anything I realize that tomorrow is not promised. Losing him changed my perspective on everything. I realized I am not here on this earth for myself, to meet certain milestones and please people. My life and focus are set on things eternal and everything that I do is evaluated and completed with God's will in mind.

## WEEK 3 — TAKE ACTION

This week ask God to help you engage in one of the activities below, or in something else that he puts on your heart. Share with the group how it felt to surrender this to the Lord.

- Pray

- Boxing

- Art

- Do something new

- Serve/give back

- Poetry – See Appendix for two beautiful poems.

- Dance

- Affirmation

- Cook

- Journal

- Advocate

- Write your testimony

- Make a video

# WEEK 3 — REFLECTION

## Participant Prayer Request

# STEP 4

## WEEK 4 ASSIGNMENTS

☐ Read answers to questions from Week 3.

☐ Read Fight for Love Principle, Scripture, Prayer, Small Group Study Overview, Week 4 Questions and Personal Testimonial.

☐ As you've committed, please be sure to complete Week 4 Small Group Study Questions in detail prior to next week's meeting.

☐ Write down personal reflections and prayer requests that come up during the week.

☐ Complete at least one activity.

## PRINCIPLE

We made a searching and fearless moral inventory of ourselves. (Baker 2007)

## SCRIPTURE

*Let us examine our ways and test them, and let us return to the Lord.*

*— Lamentations 3:40*

## PRAYER

Father in heaven, search me and reveal to me what I have hidden from myself. Help me to reflect upon the bad and the good and understand your heart in the midst of the discovery. Help me to release pain and experience joy as I journey beyond the past and toward a new life with you. In Jesus' name, amen.


## WEEK 4 — SMALL GROUP STUDY OVERVIEW

I hide birthday and Christmas presents for my family in my bedroom closet. A few times I've hidden them so well that I forget where and what they are, and sometimes I even forget that I've purchased them at all. How many of us have secrets; hidden experiences and pain that we've tucked away for so long that we're not even aware of what they are, how they happened or how they are affecting our daily lives? On the flip side, we often have dormant talents and gifts that have nearly died because our pain has drowned them out. This step gives us an opportunity to reflect on these areas with the Lord and with the support of an accountability partner or sponsor. It's important to know that it's not unusual for you to feel fear, anger, shame, sadness, depression, excitement, joy, and nostalgia as you revisit old memories. You will come out on the other side healed and stronger than you've ever been.

# WEEK 4 — SMALL GROUP STUDY QUESTIONS

Fill out the Celebrate Recovery Inventory chart (Baker 2007). Feel free to use blank paper to add more content.

*(See Appendix)*

CELEBRATE RECOVERY INVENTORY

| 1. The Person | 2. The Cause | 3. The Effect | 4. The Damage | 5. My Part |
|---|---|---|---|---|
| Who is the object of my resentment or fear? | What specific action did that person take that hurt me? | What effect didthat action haveon my life? | What damage did that action do to my social,security and/orsexual instincts? | What part of theresentment am Iresponsible for? |

1.  **THE PERSON:** Who is the object of my resent or fear?

2.  **THE CAUSE:** What specific action did the person take that hurt me?

3.  **THE EFFECT:** What effect did that action have on my life?

4.  **THE DAMAGE:** What damage was done to me socially, sexually, mentally, etc.?

5.  **MY PART:** What part, if any, of my resentment am I responsible for? Remember, if you are a victim of childhood abuse (sexual, physical, emotional, neglect, human trafficking, etc.) you are NOT GUILTY. Write "not guilty" in the chart.

In addition, I urge you to add a 6th question to the inventory. Ask what

God says about the incident and use the word of God as your guide to answer.

## TESTIMONY

One of our Survivor Leaders who graduated from our housing program is like a daughter me to me. I recently asked her to share how she was feeling as she prepared to do her inventory in Step 4.

She said,

I'm excited to walk through this process. I want to better understand my core issues that affect how I deal with and react to people. I want to understand why I seek their approval and have expectations of people and disappointments when those expectations are not met. I know that a lot of my fear has to do with not feeling accepted and wanted by my parents. There is an invisible reality in the back of my mind that tells me I'm not worthy of anything. This causes me to be eager to be loved even in unhealthy ways. Even now in my celibacy I struggle with wanting unhealthy sexual relationships and it stems into friendships as well. God is helping me to deal with this; helping me to understand how these feelings are deeply rooted in insecurity stemming from my childhood and leading me to drugs, men, and other unwanted behaviors.

We paused for a moment and then she shared an incident that will go on her chart:

"I remember one night I was on the track. I was taking some risks and got in the car with a young guy **(PERSON)**, which was against our rules. As soon as I got in car he drove to a place and tried to rape me. His car had child locks and I had to fight him off. Fortunately he had an injury and wasn't as strong as he would be normally. Somehow I got out the car and I started screaming for help. There were people around but nobody cared and no one helped. What is it in a person that makes them not care? **(PERSON)** Even though my phone was broken I was able  to make one call to my next-door neighbor who came and got    me. Sometime later I saw the guy at a store. I wanted to hurt him but I couldn't. I felt defeated and just stood there in fear and then broke down and cried. I have numbed myself now and sometimes believe that people don't care about others at all. **(THE EFFECT AND THE DAMAGE)** I realize now that that I shouldn't have been out there. **(MY PART)** It's ironic because just five years before,

I was 15 and had a friend who was in the life. I felt bad for her and told her to stop. I never thought I would end up in the same situation. I guess she influenced me. I saw that it was easy to make money and the lifestyle was common where I grew up. After that incident I never went back to the track."

After she released this we prayed. I believe God will heal her and restore her faith in him and those who he places in her path as she completes this step.

## WEEK 4 — TAKE ACTION

This week take some time to engage in one of the activities below that will allow you to release the emotions that come up when you are processing through your inventory. Physical movement is a great way to release anger. Ask the Lord to give you the strength to move the mountain.

- Pray

- Boxing

- Art

- Do something new

- Serve/give back

- Poetry – See Appendix for two beautiful poems.

- Dance

- Affirmation

- Cook

- Advocate

- Write your testimony

- Make a video

# WEEK 4 — REFLECTION

## Participant Prayer Requests

# *STEP 5*

## WEEK 5 ASSIGNMENTS

☐ Read answers to questions from Week 4

☐ Read Fight for Love Principle, Scripture, Prayer, Small Group Study Overview, Week 5 Questions and Personal Testimonial.

☐ As you've committed, please be sure to complete Week 5 Small Group Study Questions in detail prior to next week's meeting.

☐ Write down personal reflections and prayer requests that come up during the week.

☐ Complete at least one activity.

## Principle

We admitted to God, to ourselves, and to another human being the exact nature of our wrongs. (Baker 2007)

## SCRIPTURE

*Therefore confess your sins to each other and pray for each other so that you may be healed.*

*—James 5:16*

## PRAYER

Father in heaven, we come before you with pure hearts, asking that you would help us to recall people who need of our apology to heal. I pray that you would give us the words to say and help us to ensure that our words and actions are full of the love that only you can provide. In Jesus' name, amen.

## WEEK 5 — SMALL GROUP STUDY OVERVIEW

Hurt people hurt people. During this step, take the time to reflect on people you've harmed as you've been processing your own pain. These people may be ex-partners, family members, children, friends, community members, bosses, coworkers, or "they" may actually be "you."

As you reflect on the harm you have caused, ask yourself how to best seek forgiveness. Do not directly address issues with someone if it would harm them to discuss the details. For example, if your children are too young to understand addiction or human trafficking, it would be better to wait to confess.

Instead, consider writing a letter and giving it to them later or simply confessing what you did to the Lord. Rest assure the Lord forgives you and will give you peace as you release it to him

## WEEK 5 — SMALL GROUP STUDY QUESTIONS

**In Luke 23:34, Jesus says, "Father, forgive them, for they do not know what they are doing." Do you think he was referring to the things you have done or does his forgiveness only apply to others?**

**Describe a person who you would trust to hear your confessions and why.**

**Describe a few situations or relationships where it is unsafe to confess our sins and why.**

**Describe ways you can confess your shortcomings without harming another person.**

## TESTIMONY

We were at an event in San Jose, California where a well-loved survivor of human trafficking shared her story. As a teenager, she introduced her best friend to the life and they were in the streets together for a couple of years.

After a while the speaker exited the life but her best friend refused to leave and was murdered shortly thereafter by a buyer. This was devastating for the speaker; she blamed and punished herself for many years. Eventually she made amends with her deceased friend and dedicated her life to advocacy. One final step of amends was deciding to live the life she was intended to live free from condemnation and full of love

.

## WEEK 5 — TAKE ACTION

This week take some time to engage in one of the activities below that will allow you to release the emotions that have come up while planning how your will make amends. Ask God to give you the strength to move forward.

- Pray
- Boxing
- Art
- Do something new
- Serve/give back
- Poetry – See Appendix for two beautiful poems.
- Dance
- Affirmation
- Cook
- Advocate
- Write your testimony
- Make a video

# WEEK 5 — REFLECTION

## Participant Prayer Requests

# *STEP 6*

## WEEK 6 ASSIGNMENTS

☐ Read answers to questions from Week 5.

☐ Read Fight for Love Principle, Scripture, Prayer, Small Group Study Overview, Week 6 Questions and Personal Testimonial.

☐ As you've committed, please be sure to complete Week6 Small Group Study Questions in detail prior to next week's meeting.

☐ Write down personal reflections and prayer requests that come up during the week.

☐ Complete at least one activity.

## PRINCIPLE

We are entirely ready to have God remove all these defects of character. (Baker 2007)

## SCRIPTURE

*Humble yourselves before the Lord, and he will lift you up.*

*—James 4:10*

## PRAYER

Father in heaven, I am beginning to love myself and yet I have many issues that I need to work on. I pray that you will prepare me to release my defects of character to you. I know I will feel vulnerable without my old behaviors but I'm ready to try what you have designed for me instead. In Jesus' name, amen.

## WEEK 6 — SMALL GROUP STUDY OVERVIEW

To humble yourself before the Lord means to consider yourself less important and less capable than him. It's hard to admit that we think of ourselves higher than the Lord but it's true, and the depth of it is often revealed through seemingly minor actions.

For example, the Lord has spoken words of love and adoration over us and yet we continue to speak and think negatively about ourselves. We obsess and compare ourselves to others using their expectations and standards to evaluate our worth instead of using God's expectations and standards. If we will only humble ourselves we would know our true value and be set free from the things we were never meant to have, and lifted up to receive the things that are far better than that which we could ever imagine.

# WEEK 6 — SMALL GROUP STUDY QUESTIONS

What is an example of a defect of character?

Why have you been unsuccessful in changing some of your defects?

Is it possible to be humble before the Lord as suggested in James 4:10 while also standing up for yourself? Is there a difference between humbling yourself before the Lord and tolerating abuse?

In what ways was Moses humble (Numbers 12:3)? Did his humility before the Lord help him become successful?

When you think about God removing your character defects, which one are you afraid to lose and why?

## PERSONAL TESTIMONY

I've had the opportunity to mentor an AWESOME and courageous woman of God over the years. She is a survivor of abuse, domestic violence and human trafficking, and shared her perspective on what has motivated her to ask God to remove her character defects.

I knew that I was ready to have my defects of character removed by God when I realized they were hindering my growth and relationships. I wasn't able to get to where I wanted to be without surrendering them to him and realizing that light and darkness can't co-exist.

One example is the anger and rage I have struggled with for most of my adult life. The things that I've live through, like not being heard or not being seen, have made feel ignored and enraged.

I realize this stems from my childhood. As kid I didn't have a voice and I couldn't do anything about it. That brings up rage and anger for me.

Recently I realized it still comes up. One day my mother came over to visit with my kids but was reading a book the entire time while they acted out in an attempt to get her attention. That triggered a rage inside of me and I remembered when I was a kid I would beg her to notice me. She was so immersed in her books one that she didn't notice I was giving her a hickey.

These experiences have made me feel like I needed to demand the attention of those around me. The cost has been great as I've lost my peace and the quality of my relationships. In fact, I usually experience more conflict instead of the love and peaceful communication I want.

# WEEK 6 — TAKE ACTION

This week take some time to engage in one of the activities as you become ready for transformation. Ask God to give you the strength to surrender and the peace to trust him with this critical change.

- Pray

- Boxing

- Art

- Do something new

- Serve/give back

- Poetry – See Appendix for two beautiful poems.

- Dance

- Affirmation

- Cook

- Advocate

- Write your testimony

- Make a video

# WEEK 6 — REFLECTION

## Participant Prayer Requests

# *STEP 7*

**WEEK 7 ASSIGNMENTS**

☐      Read answers to questions from Week 6.

☐      Read Fight for Love Principle, Scripture, Prayer, Small Group Study Overview, Week 7 Questions and Personal Testimonial.

☐      As you've committed, please be sure to complete Week 7 Small Group Study Questions in detail prior to next week's meeting.

☐      Write down personal reflections and prayer requests that come up during the week.

☐      Complete at least one activity.

## PRINCIPLE

We humbly asked him to remove all our shortcomings. (Baker 2007)

## SCRIPTURE

*If we confess our sins, he is faithful and will forgive us our sins and purify us from all unrighteousness.— 1 John 1:9*

**PRAYER**

Father in heaven, cleanse me and renew me. Help me to fight the good fight and love myself. I have been stuck in a cycle of abuse toward myself and others. I just can't seem to move forward. I have listened to the same lies for so long I can't decipher the truth. Help me to recognize your voice and your instruction.

Purify me, God, and make me righteous so that I might walk in your perfect will. In Jesus' name, amen.

## WEEK 7 — SMALL GROUP STUDY OVERVIEW

In step 6 we prepared for God to transform us. Now it's time to ask God to "just do it." This process can sometimes feel like a root canal; first the shot, then the poking and grinding and then some blood, but in the end the tooth is saved. This process is about making a choice to turn yourself over to the Lord's correction.

Even if it means you'll suffer on a short-term basis, you'll be rid of behaviors that keep you bound and stuck in a vicious cycle of defeat.

# WEEK 7 — SMALL GROUP STUDY QUESTIONS

**What are your shortcomings that you feel are coming to an end? How can you tell God is removing them?**

**Are some shortcomings easier to release?**

**How do you feel about your shortcomings when you read Romans 8:1?**

**Are any of your sins unforgiveable?**

## TESTIMONY

When I decided to stop having sex before marriage I spent several years trying to figure out what I would do once I was ready to date. One of my character defects was a belief that I could obtain value through sex. When I gave my life to the Lord I asked God to show me how to be celibate as a single woman and place my love for God and his desire to have me to himself above my natural desires for the affection and affirmation of men.

When I started dating five years later, I had to spend a tremendous amount of energy convincing myself that I was worth talking to and that my date could actually enjoy himself in my presence without having sex. During this time, I found myself praying against thoughts that would come up as I was getting ready for a date. I would go through my closet and pick clothing with a certain thought in mind. I would say to myself, "this dress will lock him down." All the while the Holy Spirit would speak to me and help me to see that he would never send a man that I needed to lock down with a specific outfit or with a sinful behavior. I began to realize that though there is nothing wrong with being attractive, my sex appeal was not what I should lead with and was certainly not the only thing I had to offer.

## WEEK 7 — TAKE ACTION

This week take some time to engage in one of the activities as God removes your shortcomings.

- Pray

- Boxing

- Art

- Do something new

- Serve/give back

- Poetry – See Appendix for two beautiful poems.

- Dance

- Affirmation

- Cook

- Advocate

- Write your testimony

- Make a video

## WEEK 7 — REFLECTION

## Participant Prayer Requests

# *STEP 8*

**WEEK 8 ASSIGNMENTS**

- ☐ Read answers to questions from Week 7.

- ☐ Read Fight for Love Principle, Scripture, Prayer, Small Group Study Overview, Week 8 Questions and Personal Testimonial.

- ☐ As you've committed, please be sure to complete Week 8 Small Group Study Questions in detail prior to next week's meeting.

- ☐ Write down personal reflections and prayer requests that come up during the week.

- ☐ Complete at least one activity.

**PRINCIPLE**

We made a list of all persons we have harmed and became willing to make amends to them all. (Baker 2007)

**SCRIPTURE**

> *Do to others as you would have them do to you.*

> *— Luke 6:31*

## PRAYER

Father in heaven, thank you for your forgiveness and mercy.

You have covered my every sin and now you've given me an opportunity to start with a clean slate in every relationship. Thank you for loving me unconditionally. In Jesus' name, amen.

## WEEK 8 — SMALL GROUP STUDY OVERVIEW

In this step, we will create a list of those whom we have possibly harmed by our behaviors, the effect our behaviors have had on them individually, and the effect our behaviors have had on our relationships with them overall. The purpose of this step is to clear our hearts of any shame or unfinished business and release those we have harmed from any pain that they may be experiencing.

When we make amends, we are not taking responsibility for everything that has gone wrong in another person's life. In addition, there are things that the person may have done wrong to us in retaliation or while our wrong behaviors were underway, but this step is not a time to receive amends from the other person. In other words, we don't apologize to receive an apology. This is a selfless and loving action toward yourself and the people on your list. When I think of making amends, I visualize a balloon of pain moving from me to the person I have hurt, and then waiting while that person decides to release the pain to the Lord or not. They may end up rejecting the balloon, but guess what? It will still float upwards, a beautiful gift for our Father in heaven.

# WEEK 8 — SMALL GROUP STUDY QUESTIONS

Do you have expectations of the people you make amends with? What do you think will happen? What's the best thing that will happen?

What consequences do you fear in making amends?

Do you have resentment toward people you are making amends to? Will that come up as you are making your amends?

Who are the people you have harmed?

Is it safe to make amends with those you've outlined in question 4?

What kind of support do you need as you make amends with each person?

## PERSONAL TESTIMONY

A beautiful woman I know has been instrumental in teaching young ladies in the community praise dance. She is also a survivor of abuse, domestic violence and human trafficking.

She shared a story with me about the time she asked her ex-husband for forgiveness. This was hard to do because he had abused her during their marriage.

But she felt compelled to apologize when she decided to divorce him because she went into the marriage knowing that it was not going to work, and that she could not tolerate the abuse much longer. She felt bad because he had high hopes for the marriage and thought they would work together to overcome their drug addiction and alcoholism. When she decided it was over she apologized for the behaviors that had clouded her judgement and influenced her to marry him. Even so, he said he didn't forgive her. Of this she said, "that is between him and God. I feel relieved now . . . my conscious is clear."


## WEEK 8 — TAKE ACTION

This week take some time to engage in one of the activities as you reflect on those you've harmed in your pain. Remember to ask God to give you the strength to move forward. .

- Pray

- Boxing

- Art

- Do something new

- Serve/give back

- Poetry – See Appendix for two beautiful poems.

- Dance

- Affirmation

- Cook

- Advocate

- Write your testimony

- Make a video

## WEEK 8 — REFLECTION

## Participant Prayer Requests

# *STEP 9*

Week 9 Assignments

☐    Read answers to questions from Week 8.

☐    Read Fight for Love Principle, Scripture, Prayer, Small Group Study Overview, Week 9 Questions and Personal Testimonial.

☐    As you've committed, please be sure to complete Week 9 Small Group Study Questions in detail prior to next week's meeting.

☐    Write down personal reflections and prayer requests that come up during the week.

☐    Complete at least one activity.

## PRINCIPLE

We made direct amends to such people whenever possible, except when to do so would injure them or others. (Baker 2007)

## SCRIPTURE

*Therefore, if you are offering your gift at the altar and there remember that your brother has something against you, leave your gift there in front of the altar. First go and be reconciled to your brother; then come and offer your gift.*

*—Matthew 5:23-24*

## PRAYER

Father in heaven, I have so many mixed feelings about addressing these areas of the past, but I'm ready to let them go and walk forward in the fullness of life that you have designed for me. I pray that I would have the strength to make amends to all who I have harmed, such that we may have peace and healing. Be with me and give me the strength. In Jesus' name, amen.

## WEEK 9 SMALL GROUP STUDY OVERVIEW

In this step we take action and make amends to those whom we placed on our list in Step 8. We are, of course, careful not to make amends in a way that causes further harm to a person. For example, if someone is physically scared of you because you have physically abused them in the past, it would probably be better to make amends over the phone or in writing. Anything that would distract from the biblical goal of being reconciled to your brother or sister should be avoided. You may feel anxiety working up to making amends but know that God is with you and that all that you're doing is unto him.

# WEEK 9 SMALL GROUP STUDY QUESTIONS

**Those with whom you make amends may forgive you, but they may not forget. How will you respond to a person who says they forgive you but shares what you did at a later date?**

**What do you expect to experience as a result of making amends?**

**Are there people who are no longer living that you would like to make amends to? What are some ways that you can do that?**

**How do you plan to make amends with the people you have lost contact with?**

## WEEK 9 — TAKE ACTION

This week take some time to engage in one of the activities as you reflect on the process of making amends. Remember to ask God to give you the strength to move forward.

- Pray

- Boxing

- Art

- Do something new

- Serve/give back

- Poetry – See Appendix for two beautiful poems.

- Dance

- Affirmation

- Cook

- Advocate

- Write your testimony

- Make a video

## PERSONAL TESTIMONY

I grew up with a great deal of insecurity. My parents were very young when I was born, and we moved around a lot in my early years. We landed in California, thousands of miles from our family.

This combined with being bi-racial and living in poverty made me feel lost. When I finally found myself, I was very protective of my thoughts and actions and I would defend them tooth and nail. I was very selective about who I let speak into my life and would only answer to a few safe people. I think I was afraid that someone would purposely manipulate or control me. This oppositional behavior manifested in me being unable to apologize. I felt scared and anxious at the thought of admitting I was wrong, especially to someone who was unsafe and trying to control me. Instead of feeling empowered and centered, I felt scared and volatile. This changed as soon as I gave my life to the Lord. I felt protected and safe because he covered my words and my thoughts and gave me an identity that no one could take.

Now I look forward to apologizing because of the release and strength it brings.


## WEEK 9 — REFLECTION


**Participant Prayer Requests**

# *STEP 10*

**WEEK 10 ASSIGNMENTS**

☐    Read answers to questions from Week 9.

☐    Read Fight for Love Principle, Scripture, Prayer, Small Group Study Overview, Week 10 Questions and Personal Testimonial.

☐    As you've committed, please be sure to complete Week 10 Small Group Study Questions in detail prior to next week's meeting.

☐    Write down personal reflections and prayer requests that come up during the week.

☐    Complete at least one activity.

**PRINCIPLE**

We continue to take personal inventory and when we were wrong, promptly admitted it. (Baker 2007)

**SCRIPTURE**

*So, if you think you are standing firm, be careful that you don't fall!*

*— 1 Corinthians 10:12*

## PRAYER

Father in heaven, I thank you for carrying me this far. You are healing me with your loving kindness and protecting me from all the things that scare me. I commit my days to you and take inventory of the ways that I fall short. I admit that I am in desperate need of your help and guidance. Help me to live a life of freedom. In Jesus' name, amen.

## WEEK 10 SMALL GROUP STUDY OVERVIEW

Did you know that you can be delivered of one character defect and then become aware of new ones? This doesn't mean that you've failed — it means that you're alive. 2 Corinthians 3:18 says we are being transformed into the Lord's image with ever-in- creasing glory. There will always be aspects of our image that are being transformed into the image of Christ. The best thing we can do is embrace the transformation as God's loving guidance, and promptly admit when we are engaging in behaviors that are not like God.

## WEEK 10 SMALL GROUP STUDY QUESTIONS

**Day 1: Share one of the areas where you fell short today and how you addressed it.**

**Day 2:** Share one of the areas where you fell short today and how you addressed it.

**Day 3:** Share one of the areas where you fell short today and how you addressed it.

**Day 4:** Share one of the areas where you fell short today and how you addressed it.

**Day 5:** Share one of the areas where you fell short today and how you addressed it.

**Day 6:** Share one of the areas where you fell short today and how you addressed it.

## WEEK 10 — TAKE ACTION

This week take some time to engage in one of the activities as you take a daily inventory and make daily amends as needed. Remember to ask God to give you the strength to move forward.

- Pray
- Boxing
- Art

- Do something new

- Serve/give back

- Poetry – See Appendix for two beautiful poems.

- Dance

- Affirmation

- Cook

- Advocate

- Write your testimony

- Make a video

Recently I experienced a major breakthrough regarding my health. For most of my life I have stressed about my weight and looks and feared abandonment if I wasn't perfect. I think this stemmed from years of distorted words spoken to me by partners and friends. I was made to believe I was only as valuable as the brand of my clothing, the money in my pocket or the status of the man I was with. When I first gave my life to the Lord, I was healed of the belief that I had to have sex with my boyfriend to keep him. But there was still a root that remained. A root that that lied to me and told me I was an object instead of God's beloved daughter. Recently the Lord showed me *Psalm 139:*

*13 For you created my inmost being; you knit me together in my mother's womb. 14 I praise you because I am fearfully and wonderfully made; your works are wonderful, I know that full well. 15 My frame was not hidden from you when I was made in the secret place, when I was woven together in the depths of the earth. 16 Your eyes saw my unformed body; all the days ordained for me were written in your book before one of them came to be. 17 How precious to me are your thoughts. How vast is the sum of them! 18 Were I to count them, they would outnumber the grains of sand — when I awake, I am still with you.*

I have seen the scripture many times before but this time it broke me. I started crying. I realized that I had spoken ill words about God's creation . . . about his beloved. That I had embraced a lie about who I was. So now I take inventory each day of the lies that  I have allowed in and promptly admit that they are not true. God   is teaching me to deeply love what he created . . . ME.

# WEEK 10 REFLECTION NOTES

## Participant Prayer Requests

# STEP 11

## WEEK 11 ASSIGNMENTS

☐ Read answers to questions from Week 10.

☐ Read Fight for Love Principle, Scripture, Prayer, Small Group Study Overview, Week 11 Questions and Personal Testimonial.

☐ As you've committed, please be sure to complete Week 11 Small Group Study Questions in detail prior to next week's meeting.

☐ Write down personal reflections and prayer requests that come up during the week.

☐ Complete at least one activity.

## PRINCIPLE

We sought through prayer and meditation to improve our conscious contact with God, praying only for knowledge of His will for us, and power to carry that out. (Baker 2007)

## SCRIPTURE

*Let the word of Christ dwell in you richly.*

*—Colossians 3:16*

## PRAYER

Father in heaven, I love you and I trust you. I want to get to know you even more and know you for myself. I pray you would reveal your perfect will and purpose for my life and give me the power to carry it out. In Jesus' name, amen. .

## WEEK 11 SMALL GROUP STUDY OVERVIEW

What is life without purpose? A joy ride or a life that dead ends? The only way to know our purpose is to ask the one who created us to reveal it. The challenge with purpose is it is revealed over time, and many of us are unwilling to wait. So we create our own reality and find ourselves running into a wall in a neighborhood we were never intended to visit. In this step, we learn to rely on the word of Christ and pray over it diligently until his purpose becomes clear.

## WEEK 11 SMALL GROUP STUDY QUESTIONS

**How often do you read the word? What hinders you and what encourages you?**

**How do you pray? Do you feel obligated to pray for a certain amount of time?**

Take this spiritual gifts assessment: www.spiritualgiftstest.com. How do your gifts align with your purpose?

Do your relationships and activities align with the purpose that God is revealing to you?

How do you tap into the power of God for strength?

## WEEK 11 — TAKE ACTION

This week take some time to engage in one of the activities as you read God's word, pray and reflect on your purpose.

Remember to ask God to give you the power to move forward.

- Pray

- Boxing

- Art

- Do something new

- Serve/give back

- Poetry – See Appendix for two beautiful poems.

- Dance

- Affirmation

- Cook

- Advocate

- Write your testimony

- Make a video

## PERSONAL TESTIMONY

When I first came to the Lord I was invited by a group of women to pray at church at six in the morning. I wasn't thrilled at the invitation. First of all, I disliked mornings in general, and second, I was scared to pray out loud. I was scared because didn't know the bible very well and was afraid I would be required to quote scripture or use one of those fancy "ETH" words. Despite my fear, I agreed to pray when I was called on. As I suspected it would be, it was uncomfortable. I was confused and struggled to express my thoughts. Thinking back, I realize that I was really praying to the women that day and trying to impress them instead of God. Today I pray freely and many times my prayer is one word. I don't need the validation of people to know that my message is getting through to the one who can touch my life.

# WEEK 11 REFLECTION NOTES

## Participant Prayer Requests

# *STEP 12*

## WEEK 12 ASSIGNMENTS

- [ ] Read answers to questions from Week 11.

- [ ] Read Fight for Love Principle, Scripture, Prayer, Small Group Study Overview, Week 12 Questions and Personal Testimonial.

- [ ] As you've committed, please be sure to complete Week 12 Small Group Study Questions in detail prior to next week's meeting.

- [ ] Write down personal reflections and prayer requests that come up during the week.

- [ ] Complete at least one activity.

## PRINCIPLE

Having had a spiritual experience as the result of these steps, we try to carry this message to others and practice these principles in all our affairs. (Baker 2007)

## SCRIPTURE

*Brothers, if someone is caught in a sin, you who are spiritual should restore them gently. But watch yourself, or you also may be tempted.*

*– Galatians 6:1*

## PRAYER

Father in heaven, put people in my life who I can share this message with and equip me with the time and wisdom to minister to them just as you equipped my sponsor/accountability partner to minister to me. I pray you would cover my mind and my heart as I make contacts, and reveal to me who you have assigned to my life for this awesome opportunity. In Jesus' name, amen.

## WEEK 12 SMALL GROUP STUDY OVERVIEW

This step is a beautiful time to look back on how far you've come. As you do this, a few people will pop into your mind and you'll wish they could receive a similar healing. The good news is that they can. This program was designed to share, and it's the perfect gift for someone you love. Take a moment to make a list of people and begin to pray for them. In this step it is easy to become co-dependent and give up our safe boundaries and healthy behaviors in order to save others. Instead of rushing to give your gift away, continue to fight to love yourself and pray that God would give you the words to share your gift in a way that is healthy and effective.

# WEEK 12 SMALL GROUP STUDY QUESTIONS

**Who are some of the people in your life that could benefit from God's healing?**

**What healthy boundaries will you establish with people who have asked you to be their sponsor/accountability partner?**

**What excites you about carrying this message to others?**

**What scares you about carrying this message to others?**

## WEEK 12 — TAKE ACTION

This week take some time to engage in one of the activities and invite the person that the Lord is encouraging you to minister to. Remember to ask God to give you the power to move forward.

- Pray
- Boxing
- Art

- Do something new

- Serve/give back

- Poetry – See Appendix for two beautiful poems.

- Dance

- Affirmation

- Cook

- Advocate

- Write your testimony

- Make a video


**TESTIMONY**

I had the great honor of supporting a dear sister as she walked through the 12 steps. She is a survivor of abuse, domestic violence and human trafficking. Here is what she shared about her 12th step:

I had tried both Alcoholic Anonymous and Narcotics Anonymous but adding God to the picture was different. When I tried to work my steps the other two times I would get stuck in Step 4. I was stuck without the support of the Lord. When I handed Step 4 over to God I experienced a weight being lifted off of me.

I was given a fresh slate and my freedom. I must admit it was an extremely painful experience, but I didn't want to do it half way. I realized I was only as sick as my darkest secret. Let me tell you, I was really thorough. I wanted to talk about my abuser and not have it take me out for days. In the past if I talked about him I would experience a Post-Traumatic Stress Disorder (PTSD) episode and literally would not be able to function for the rest of the day. At times I would be triggered and could not complete my work.

Now I can share my story with others who have been abused as I was, and relive the initial purifying experience as they experience it for the first time.

I'm convinced God wants us to share our story to help others feel confident enough to release their secrets. It is scary to think about how people will judge you. But I like to remind myself that we are all broken in one way or another, and while I was going through my steps I was surrounded by people who love and understand me. The hardest part about working the steps was being vulnerable. I'm grateful I was able to do that in a safe place. Since that time, I have walked two women through their steps.

As I incorporated my experience with the steps I helped them to open up, feel comfortable and know that they are not alone. And it helped me to replay the tape and remember where I once was and how far God has brought me.

# WEEK 12 REFLECTION NOTES

## Participant Prayer Requests

# SUMMARY

Over the last 12 weeks we've learned so much. As you receive your healing, I pray that you would not only receive it for yourself, but that you would also connect with other survivors of abuse, domestic violence and/or human trafficking and pray for them.

Tell them they are not alone. Remind them that we serve a mighty God who unfolds our purpose even while we are in pain, and many times will call us to agree with him for the healing of others who suffer just as we did.

**_Whom the son sets free is free indeed!_**

# *FACILITATOR BEST PRACTICES*

Fight for Love Small Group leaders must be spirit filled, compassionate, empathetic, discerning, and clear on personal boundaries. It is not necessary for facilitators to have experienced abuse, domestic violence or human trafficking as God has assigned many people with different experiences to walk alongside those who are hurting in our communities.

You can access the Fight For Love Facilitator Guide online at

*https://vimeo.com/283852671.*

You can also purchase the Author Facilitated Video

*http://loveneverfailsus.com/shop .*

**Step 1 Facilitator Note:** The purpose of this step is for the participants to assess their level of self-awareness and reliance on the power of the Lord. As a facilitator, observe whether the participants know what their purpose is, and the impact that their behaviors are having on them fulfilling it.

**Step 2 Facilitator Note:** The purpose of this step is to contrast the difference between living life by one's own power versus living by the power of God. Can the participants feel any difference between the two, and if so, what difference does that make on the outcomes in their lives?

**Step 3 Facilitator Note:** The purpose of this step is to assess the participants' ability to surrender to God. Why is this easy or difficult? Survivors of abuse, domestic violence and human trafficking are sometimes used to relinquishing all control to someone else but become resentful about it later. During this step, participants must learn to surrender to a loving God, not a God of judgement and control.

**Step 4 Facilitator Note:** The purpose of this step is to assist and support the participants in releasing their pain and resentments. It is very important to take good care of yourself during this step as the stories that survivors share will often be very painful to hear. You will need your own support system to provide you with the proper level of care during this step. Also, know that survivors of abuse, domestic violence and human trafficking have been taught by their abusers to minimize their abuse and feel responsible for those who have abused them. They engage in a great deal of self-blame in order to cope with what has been done to them. Research trauma bonding for more information on some of the responses that may present themselves. Some participants will feel as though they are betraying their abuser if they mention any harm that the abuse caused during their step four inventory. They should also be encouraged to document the pain that the abuser caused and know that it will not ever be shared with the abuser unless they agree to do so. There are a few exceptions, such as the abuse of a child.

**Steps 5-9 Facilitator Note:** The purpose of these steps is to assist and support the participants as they contemplate how their actions have harmed others. It's important to note that survivors of abuse, domestic violence and human trafficking have been taught by their abusers to minimize the abuse and feel responsible for those who have abused them. This is part of trauma bonding and can come up and cause participants to feel as though they are betraying their abuser if they mention any harm that they caused. Somewhere in this process, participants should come to a new realization that they can make amends to someone who harmed them for the part they played in a scenario without taking full responsibility for the abuse that was committed against them. They should also be encouraged to document the pain that the abuser caused and know that it will not ever be shared with the abuser unless they do the sharing.

The only exception to this rule is child abuse and/or active domestic violence or human trafficking.

**Step 10 Facilitator Note:** The purpose of this step is to raise participants' awareness about daily challenges and encourage loving responses to mistakes that are made so that they remain on track. People who have been highly traumatized tend to have extreme responses to criticism. Either they completely discount what they see or they let the smallest mistake derail all their efforts. The goal of this step is stay in the middle — fight for love and know that we serve a God that is not a stranger to sin or mistakes.

**Step 11 Facilitator Note:** The purpose of this step is to encourage the participants to use God's word, prayer and relationship with God to understand and fulfill their purpose. Because there have been so many others providing false purposes, this make take a while. Reassurance from the facilitator is key.

**Step 12 Facilitator Note:** The purpose of this step is to encourage participants to engage others in their healing journey while also maintaining their own boundaries. Because survivors are used to giving themselves up to please someone else, they need additional discussion and reminders that they can say no, as well as encouragement to step out and engage.

# *APPENDIX*

## 12 STEPS SIMPLIFIED

1. Admit you have a problem.

2. Believe Jesus can fix it.

3. Turn your life over to Jesus.

4. Write down everything that hurts and how the pain started.

5. Admit what, if anything, you did wrong.

6. Get ready to change.

7. Ask Jesus to change you for the better.

8. Make a list of those you harmed.

9. Make amends to those you harmed.

10. Notice and admit when you're wrong.

11. Improve our relationship with Jesus, understand his purpose and pray for the power to fulfill it.

12. Now that you've experienced healing, share this with someone else.

# CELEBRATE RECOVERY 12 STEPS AND BIBLICAL COMPARISONS (BAKER 2007)

1. We admitted we were powerless over our addictions and compulsive behaviors, that our lives had become unmanageable.

   *I know that nothing good lives in me, that is, in my sinful nature. For I have the desire to do what is good, but I cannot carry it out.*

   *—Romans 7:18 NIV*

2. We came to believe that a power greater than ourselves could restore us to sanity.

   *For it is God who works in you to will and to act according to his good purpose. — Philippians 2:13 NIV*

3. We made a decision to turn our lives and our wills over to the care of God.

   *Therefore, I urge you, brothers, in view of God's mercy, to offer your bodies as living sacrifices, holy and pleasing to God — this is your spiritual act of worship. —Romans 12:1 NIV*

4. We made a searching and fearless moral inventory of ourselves.

   *Let us examine our ways and test them, and let us return to the Lord.— Lamentations 3:40 NIV*

5. We admitted to God, to ourselves, and to another human being the exact nature of our wrongs.

> *Therefore confess your sins to each other and pray for each other so that you may be healed. —James 5:16a NIV*

6. We were entirely ready to have God remove all these defects of character.

> *Humble yourselves before the Lord, and he will lift you up.*
>
> *—James 4:10 NIV*

7. We humbly asked him to remove all of our shortcomings.

> *If we confess our sins, he is faithful and will forgive us our sins and purify us from all unrighteousness. — 1 John 1:9 NIV*

8. We made a list of all persons we have harmed and became willing to make amends to them all.

> *Do to others as you would have them do to you. —Luke 6:31 NIV*

9. We made direct amends to such people whenever possible, except when to do so would injure them, ourselves, or others.

> *Therefore, if you are offering your gift at the altar and there remember that your brother has something against you, leave your gift there in front of the altar. First go and be reconciled to your brother; then come and offer your gift.*
>
> *—Matthew 5:23-24NIV*

10. We continued to take personal inventory and when we wrong promptly admitted it.

> *So, if you think you are standing firm, be careful that you don't fall! — 1 Corinthians 10:12*

11. We sought through prayer and meditation to improve our conscious contact with God, praying only for knowledge of his will for us, and power to carry that out.

> *Let the word of Christ dwell in you richly. —Colossians 3:16aNIV*

12. Having had a spiritual experience as the result of these steps, we try to carry this message to others and practice these principles in all our affairs

> *Brothers, if someone is caught in a sin, you who are spiritual should restore them gently. But watch yourself, or you also may be tempted. —Galatians 6:1NIV*

# BEAUTY IS US

## BY SABLE HORTON

Beauty What is it?

This thing that every girl strives to be

That society determines only by things we can see Even if

those things aren't really me

This thing that that I crave so desperately

Yet forget that I was created with true beauty dwelling inside

of me Somewhere along the line, the true essence of beauty

has been changed

Redefined

It's been rewritten Molded by lies

Shaped by so many young girls' cries Causing self-esteem

lows and highs

To reach this level of beauty that we were indeed born with

We think we have to lose weight to achieve it

Cover up our skin to appear as it Dress a certain way to obtain

it

Make our bodies available to all to be labeled as it

We no longer listen to the ultimate Master who created us all

as masterpieces

Instead we cut and snip ourselves apart into tiny pieces In

order to fit into the box of what we think beauty is

It was never meant to be like this

We're drowning in false beauty standards and fighting to stay afloat When we starve ourselves we are really starving our hopes, dreams and aspirations

Allowing the enemies schemes and perversions to come on in

It's time that we stop giving into these lies

The truth is that none of us have to strive for beauty We are already so beautiful

We are set apart beings that God handpicked Himself

He made us perfect in His eyes and we are still the apple of them It doesn't matter what our hair looks like or what we wear

For we are dressed in Gods garments of blessings and love already

We are vessels for honor and God places tiaras on us Our dad is a king, ladies, we are royalty

We are more valuable than any dollar amount We are so beautiful that no product can contain it

We are so beautiful that no ad can capture it We are so beautiful that no trend can measure it

When you look in the mirror see yourself through His eyes My sisters

You are bold, blissful, blessed, and built in His sight

You are excellent, enough, and loved by Him with all His might You are accepted, amazing, abiding in love and the apple of His eye You are unique, useful, and represent unending joy despite potential cries

You are tolerant, triumphant, thankful, and teachable

You are incredible, intelligent, inquisitive, and with God

invincible You are fabulous, fantastic, and fearfully and

wonderfully made You are unashamed, unshaken, and

represent unwavering faith because Jesus has always stayed

You are laughter, liveliness, and represent love because what

God says about you is true

So I say again Beauty

What is it? It is you

# FIGHT FOR LOVE

**BY BELOVED ALVAREZ**

Broken.

That is what "Love" has been for me.

So broken

that I haven't known how to fix it.

Oh, I know I've tried.

Pathetically.

Passionately.

Desperately.

And fearfully.

I have not failed for trying.

But I have failed at the single,

most critical point, when it comes to love:

Letting go.


Because there has been this broken

root

down deep in the pit of my soul,

that tries so hard to hold on

to everything I know –

so that even "letting go"

becomes holding on,

and releasing

always turns to retaining

some measure of control

over what has access to my heart.

And I am tired
of being broken.
I am
ready to let go
of holding on,
and to discover
something so much greater
than I,
in my brokenness,
have known.

Love.
Love that is
Patient.
Kind.
Gentle.
Preserving,
even when I am undeserving.
Good,
even when I am bad.
Cherishing,
even when I cannot see my own worth.
Love
that does not depend on me
for its survival.

I want to open myself up to

a love that is

never manipulating,

never destructive,

never untrustworthy, n

ever emptying.

A love that never leaves me with less than I came in with.


A love that has called to me since the womb of my existence.


A love that I forsook,

to taste always something less.


I want to know the love that has pursued me down into the

depths of my ravaged darkness;

the darkness I have cultivated and learned to make my home.

The darkness that now feels like comfort to me,

this walled-in shelter in which I would be

content to stay . . .


Except that there is One Who always comes knocking here . . .

He is not content that I should remain,

and is always

and ever

seeking to draw me out of my bed

made of pain.

He has

more

and better

for me,

He claims . . .


I want to live in the love that has held out its warm hands to

me for as long as I can remember.

With every shattered illusion, those hands reached in.

With every crushed hope, they invited me back into the safety

of truth.

With every blow to my broken identity, they came, pierced

with the marks of their own brokenness,

reminding me that there was a place of redemption still

waiting for me,

a place where all my ashes could still be turned into fierce

beauty.


I want to abandon these bars of resistance, this vow of my

reinforced disbelief in love.

I want to forsake the control I have set up

to keep me "safe" from the vulnerabilities of love.

Because that control has become a monster,

an enemy of the one thing I most need and yet deeply fear.

And I don't want it here,

anymore.


Because

relentless is the compelling force of this love toward my

broken heart.

And for all of the caution my control is throwing up like red

flags on a dead end road,

love has already begun to have its way -

pulling me out of measure and into fullness,

out of shadows and into truth,

out of something and into SomeOne

Who has the power to change everything.

I can feel it,

I can feel Him,

moving in...


Even where my faith is faltering, d

eterred by deep-seated memories

I cannot dig my way through,

Love has hooked me.

And all of my resistance,

like an avalanche of years and tears,

built to protect my wounds,

is giving way to the sight of promise,

somehow.


I have been here before,

where the ground gives way to a sliver of light.

It is a familiar trembling that my heart knows well.

If history voices its argument in this hour, retreat is

inevitable, For my strongholds have been built from its

repeated disappointments.

There is truth to the claims which have supported and

strengthened

my walls.


Still,

there is a stronger voice which speaks –

a greater argument,

from a greater history

rising up to tell its truth,

and my soul is finding it hard to resist

the claims that have come to tear down my walls . . .

I have hidden here for so long.

The thought of leaving indeed inspires terror,

and yet I am drawn to the edges of my cage.

Risk fills the air around me like the putrid stench of death

looming on a hazy horizon.

Do I dare to take this step?

I am familiar with what's at stake.

I know well the cost of agreeing to come out, of giving my

heart over once again.


But this is an undeniable moment of choice... and while my

heart is shouting: Stay safe!",

a voice that is deeper than my pain is whispering "I know

you," and somehow that feels more like home to me than

anything ever has.


So I walk to the edge of this place I have known for so many

years, preparing my heart to say goodbye.

I have,

undeniably,

been called to a new place,

to a new day.

And somehow, by a strength and a hope that are not my own,

I believe in the Love that lives there.

And I want to go.

No matter what it costs me.


With a deep, releasing breath,

I choose to let go.

I am letting go,

renouncing my age-old friend,

control,

and stepping into covenant with a new power,

a power not my own;

a power so much greater than I have ever known.


With all of Heaven, I agree:

Love will have its way in me!

And, forever, my life will tell a new story:

the story of how love was always meant to be.


Jesus, I surrender to the fight You have won for me.

I believe, Jesus.

I believe in the power of your love to heal me,


August 29, 2018

| 1. THE PERSON | 2. THE CAUSE | 3. THE EFFECT | 4. THE DAMAGE | 5. MY PART | 6. BIBLICAL INSIGHT |
|---|---|---|---|---|---|
| Who is the object of my resentment or fear? | What specific action did that person take that hurt me? | What effect did that action have on my life? | What damage did that action do to my social, security and/or sexual instincts? | What part of the resentment am I responsible for? | What does God say about it? |

# REFERENCES

Baker, Richard D. Warrent and John E. 2007. Life's Healing Choices; Freedom from Your Hurts, Hang-ups and Habits . Howard Books.

DOJ. 1999. Raising awareness about sexual abuse. Accessed May 12, 2018. https://www.nsopw.gov/en-US/Education/ FactsStatistics?AspxAutoDetectCookieSupport=1.

Leshner, Dr. Alan I. 1998. National Institute on Drug Abuse. July 01. Accessed May 12, 2018. https:// archives.drugabuse.gov/news-events/nida-notes/nida-probes-elusive-link-between-child-abuse-later-drug-abuse.

Nations, United. 2018. United Nations Office on Drugs and Crime. May 12. Accessed May 12, 2018. https://www.unodc.org/unodc/en/ human-trafficking/what-is-human-trafficking.html.

Polaris. 2017. National Human Trafficking Hotline. Accessed May 12, 2018. https://humantraffickinghotline.org/states.

S., Ruth. 2012. May 16. Accessed Jan 20, 2018. https://domesticviolencestatistics.org/men-the-overlooked-victims-of-domestic-violence/#comments.

USDHHS. 2006. Child Abuse and Neglect Statistics. Accessed May 12, 2018. https://www.childwelfare.gov/topics/systemwide/ statistics/can/.

Made in the USA
Las Vegas, NV
16 August 2022

53329418R00063